STARTERS FOR VIOLIN

17 arrangements and original pieces
with piano accompaniment

LIONEL SALTER

THE ASSOCIATED BOARD OF
THE ROYAL SCHOOLS OF MUSIC

£3·50

CONTENTS

STARTERS FOR VIOLIN
MENUET

Arranged by
Lionel Salter

LULLY

This minuet, famous as that used by the dancing-master in Molière's *Le bourgeois gentilhomme*, was in fact written for another *comédie-ballet* by him some months previously, *Les amants magnifiques*.

BEST FOOT FORWARD

LIONEL SALTER

MENUET

Arranged by
Lionel Salter

HANDEL

[♩ = 112]

From the *Musick for the Royal Fireworks*, composed in 1749 to celebrate the Peace of Aix-la-Chapelle.

OF STRANGE LANDS AND PEOPLES

Arranged by
Lionel Salter

SCHUMANN, Op.15 No.1

Schumann's original metronome marking (♩ = 108) for this first piece in his *Kinderscenen* seems very questionable, and out of keeping with the character of the music.

A LEGEND

LIONEL SALTER

O WILLY'S RARE

Arranged by
Lionel Salter

SCOTTISH TRADITIONAL

EVENING

LIONEL SALTER

OLD FRENCH SONG

Arranged by
Lionel Salter

TCHAIKOVSKY, Op.39 No.16

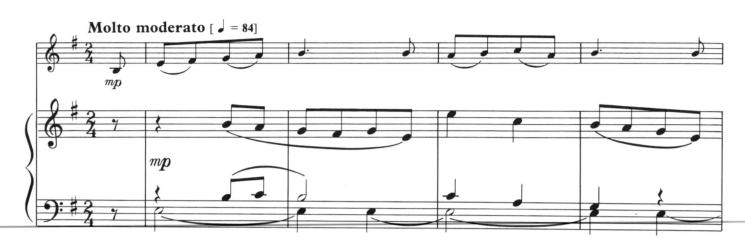

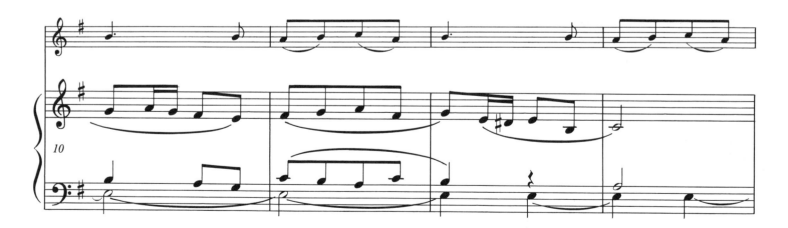

The original piano piece, from Tchaikovsky's *Album for the Young*, is in G minor. In arranging it for the violin the texture accompanying the melody has been amplified.

WE HAVE A NEW MASTER

Arranged by
Lionel Salter

J. S. BACH

This is the opening duet of the 'Peasant Cantata', BWV 212, written in 1742 to celebrate the arrival of a new lord of the manor of two villages near Leipzig.

PASSEPIED

Arranged by
Lionel Salter

attrib. LEOPOLD MOZART

Leopold Mozart took great pains over his children's musical education. In 1759 he put together a 'notebook' for his first child Nannerl, then aged eight: three years later he made a similar collection for his six-year-old son Wolfgang. It is from the latter that this piece (originally for keyboard) is taken.

GAVOTTE

Arranged by
LIONEL SALTER

HANDEL

This movement, arranged from Handel's trio-sonata Op. 5 No. 3, had already been used in the revised version of his opera *Il pastor fido*. If desired, the F♯ minims in bars 20–22 may also be played trilled (as in the original).

CHATTERBOX

LIONEL SALTER

WHAT SWEET CONTENT

Arranged by
Lionel Salter

attrib. J. S. BACH

This aria ('Wie wohl ist mir') comes from Bach's second book of pieces written out in 1725 for his wife Anna Magdalena. The words begin: 'What sweet content, O Friend of souls, when in Thy love I rest'.

MENUET and TRIO

Arranged by
Lionel Salter

MOZART, K.61b/1

On the evening before his 13th birthday, Mozart wrote seven minuets and trios for two violins and bass, of which this is the first. The key was originally G major.

TRIO

Menuet D.C. al Fine

BOURRÉE

TELEMANN

From 'A Musico-choreographic Wedding Divertissement', about 1750. The realisation of the bass is by the editor.

WALTZ TIME

LIONEL SALTER

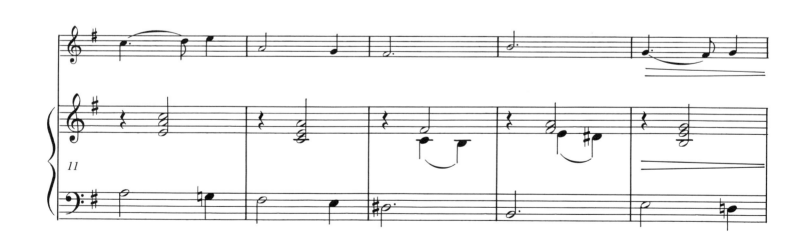

GAVOTTE

Arranged by
Lionel Salter

COUPERIN

From the Premier Ordre ('La Françoise') of *Les Nations*, originally for two violins and continuo.

Printed in England by Caligraving Limited Thetford Norfolk AB 2022